BUSY LITTLE
ARTIST

Sally Hewitt ● Illustrated by Penny Dann

CONRAN OCTOPUS

This book belongs to

Design: Alison Fenton
Design assistants: Karen Fenton
and Caroline Johnson
Spine illustration: Alison Barclay
Editor: Sue Hook
Photography: Mike Galletly

The author and publishers would like to thank
Val Abercrombie and the children who made the projects
to be photographed: Harriet Bates, Elizabeth de Gatacre,
Alice Jarvis, Claire Linnette, Madeleine O'Shea,
Rebecca Rand, Jemma Rowe, Camilla Sutton

First published in 1990 by
Conran Octopus Limited
37 Shelton Street, London WC2H 9HN

Reprinted in 1993

© text 1990 Conran Octopus Limited
© illustration 1990 Penny Dann

ISBN 1 85029 272 8

Typeset by Creative Text Limited.
Printed and bound in Singapore

Contents

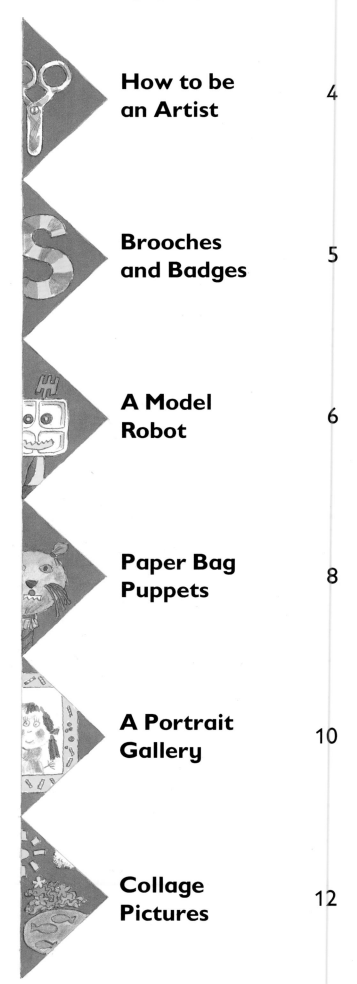

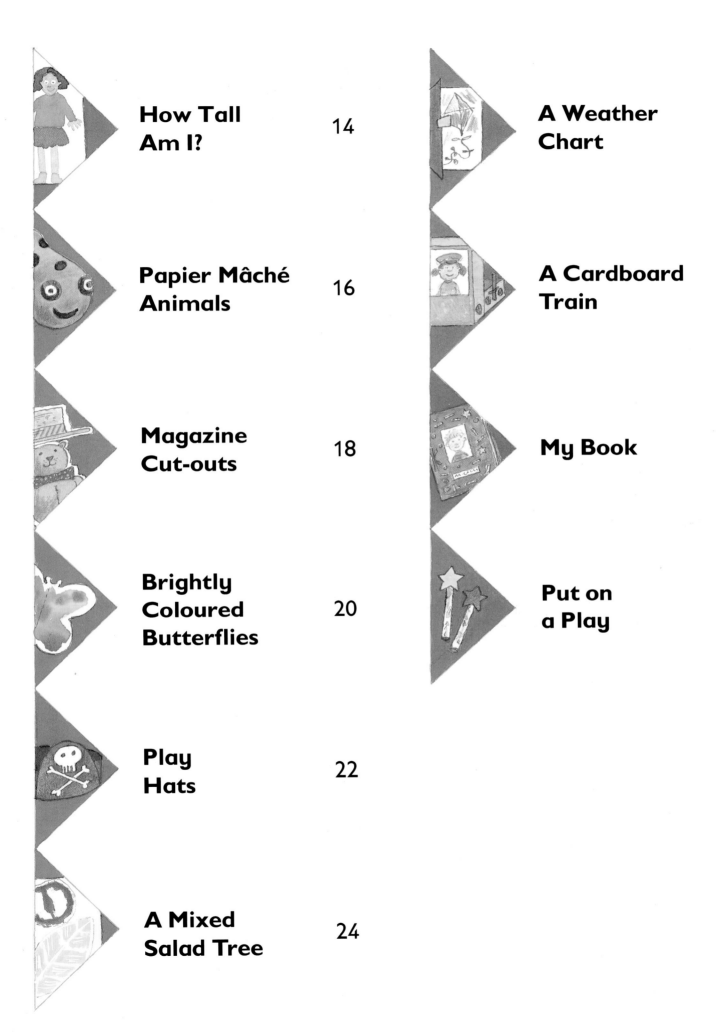

How to be an Artist

Do you like cutting and sticking, drawing and painting, tearing and folding and making interesting things? Bits and pieces, busy hands and lots of ideas are all you need to be an artist. Ask an adult to help you whenever you see this symbol ★.

▶ Find out how you can be an artist

Get a box for your tools. Put a pencil, crayons, round-ended scissors, paint and glue brushes, sticky tape, empty yoghurt pots, glue and some paints into your box.

What would you like to make? A present for a friend, a decoration for your room, a robot or a puppet? Now you've got your tools, materials and ideas.

You will need a bigger box for your materials. Collect lots of interesting things: different sorts of paper, buttons, beads, shells, empty boxes, cardboard rolls, wool, pretty pieces of fabric, magazines and cards. What else can you think of?

Are you ready to be an artist?

Take care!
Do make very sure that younger children can't get hold of small items that you are collecting or using.

Brooches and Badges

Make a badge of your own age or initial and decorate it yourself.

You will need

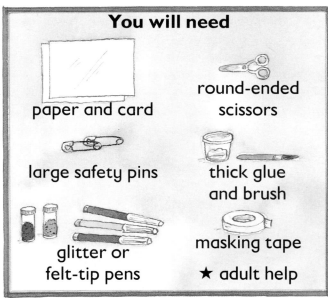

paper and card

round-ended scissors

large safety pins

thick glue and brush

glitter or felt-tip pens

masking tape

★ adult help

Birthday presents

Make birthday presents for your friends. Make a badge of their initials or age. You can pin the badge to a birthday card you have made for them.

1 Draw the first letter of your name or the number of your age on a piece of card. You can draw round a plastic letter or number if you have one.

2 Cut out the letter or number and decorate it. You can paint it with glue and sprinkle on glitter or colour it in.

3 ★ Stick the safety pin to the back of the badge with a piece of masking tape. Press the tape down firmly.

A Model Robot

Don't throw away empty boxes, packets or cardboard rolls. Use them to make a model. You can even make it move!

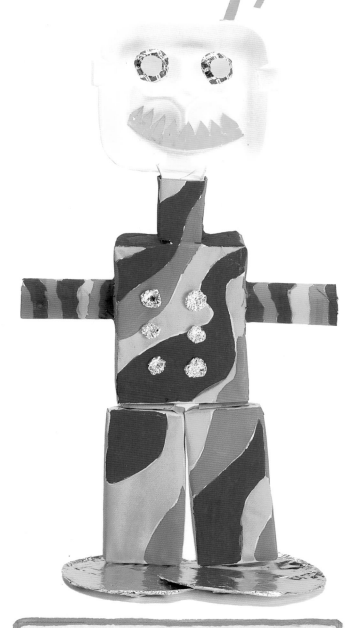

You will need

a collection of boxes, cardboard rolls and decorating materials

round-ended scissors

masking tape

lining paper

thick glue and brush

paints, water and brushes

Cardboard rolls are good for arms.

I'll use this big box for the body.

1 Set your boxes and rolls out on the table in the shape you want for your robot.

Some more ideas

Try making a boat that floats. Don't paint it! Make a truck with wheels that go round, a space ship or a totem pole decorated with feathers.

2 Wrap the boxes up in lining paper, like a parcel, so that they are easier to paint. Use masking tape to stick the paper in place over the boxes.

4 You can cut out rectangles of cardboard and bend them in the middle to make a moving joint. Use masking tape to stick one side of the joint to the leg and one side to the body.

3 Stick the boxes firmly together. Snip round the end of the cardboard roll to make flaps. Press the flaps out to make a flat surface for sticking with thick glue. Stick the cardboard rolls in place.

5 Decorate your robot with milk bottle tops, tin foil and card to make eyes, knobs and aerials. Paint it brightly with several colours. What are you going to call it?

Paper Bag Puppets

Use paper bags to make puppets, and put on a show for your friends.

You will need

paper bags

coloured paper

crumpled up newspaper

round-ended scissors

elastic bands

masking tape

cardboard rolls

thick glue and brush

wool

★ adult help

This is going to be a pig.

These pointed ears look like a fox.

1 ★ Make ears by twisting elastic bands just below the top 2 corners of the paper bag. Make sure you don't tear the bag.

2 ▶ Stuff crumpled up newspaper inside the bag. You can put an extra piece in where you want the nose to be.

4 ▶ Decorate the head with glued coloured paper to make the face. Cut wool whiskers and fix with masking tape.

3 ▶ Push a cardboard roll up into the newspaper and pull the bottom of the bag down over the roll. ★ Twist an elastic band round the bag and the roll to hold them firmly together.

Put on a puppet show

When you have made several puppets, make up a story about them. Hide behind the back of a chair and hold the puppets over the top. You can act out your story for your friends.

A Portrait Gallery

A portrait is a picture that looks like someone. Draw a picture of your friend.

You will need

pencil

coloured paper or card

smaller piece of white paper

crayons

thick glue and brush

bits for decorating

hole punch

You've got blue eyes.

Yours are brown.

1 Look carefully at your friend's face before you start your picture.

Your face is this shape.

It looks like an egg!

2 Draw the shape of the face on the white paper. Use a pencil.

3 Draw the face and hair using the right colours.

4 Turn the paper over. Put small blobs of glue on the corners and middle. Stick your portrait on the coloured card, leaving a border round the edge.

5 Punch 2 holes in the top edge of the frame. Stick on shells, buttons, beads or cut-up drinking straws.

Hang your portrait

Thread wool or ribbon through the holes in the frame. Name your portrait and hang it on the wall.

Collage Pictures

Collect different materials and use them to make a collage picture for your wall.

Here are some ideas for your collection:

1 Feel the different textures of the things you have collected. What picture can you use them for?

You will need

thick paper and card

collected materials

thick glue and brush

round-ended scissors

2 If you are using sand or glitter, spread glue on to your thick paper and sprinkle the sand or glitter on to the glue.

3 Cut bits of paper or material into the shapes you want. Glue the backs and stick them on to your paper.

4 When you have finished, frame your picture and hang it with your portrait.

Some more ideas for collage pictures

Make a snow scene with cotton wool, glitter and paper doilies.

Make a feely pattern using things that feel different.

Make an underwater picture with blue and green tissue-paper sea and sweet-paper fish.

How Tall Am I?

Make a chart for your bedroom to see how tall you are. Keep a record of your height.

You will need

2 x 1½ metre lengths of lining paper

newspaper

1 dark crayon

paints, water and brushes

round-ended scissors

cold-water paste and brush

masking tape

ruler

2 Take your shoes off. Lie down on the paper with your hands by your sides and your feet out sideways. Get your friend to draw round you with a thick crayon.

1 Cut 2 x 1½ metre lengths of lining paper. Lay one sheet on the kitchen floor. Fix each corner with a piece of masking tape.

3 Spread newspaper over the floor under your drawing. Paint in the figure so that it looks just like you.

4 When the painting is dry, cut round it carefully and put it paint side down on the newspaper. Brush cold-water paste all over the back and then stick it on to your second length of paper.

5 Write HOW TALL AM I? at the top and stick the chart on the wall so the bottom touches the floor. Mark equally spaced measurements up one side.

Another idea for measuring

Cut and colour the shape of your hand-span. Stick the shapes up the side of the chart. How many hands high are you?

Papier Mâché Animals

Papier mâché objects are strong and easy to make. Try making some animals using balloons as moulds.

You will need

bowl

cold-water paste and brush

round-ended scissors

sheets of newspaper

blown-up balloon tied with string

paints, water and brushes

This one looks like a caterpillar.

I like this big fat one.

1 Spread newspaper on the table. Tear some more newspaper into strips. Choose a balloon. What kind of animal could you make it into?

2 ▶ Brush cold-water paste on to the newspaper strips and cover the balloon evenly with them. Repeat this until there are about 3 layers of newspaper pasted on the balloon.

4 ▶ When it is quite dry, it will feel hard when you tap it. Use paints to colour it brightly all over. Don't forget to wash your brush before you use a new colour.

3 ▶ Hang the balloon up to dry somewhere cool and airy. It will take at least a day before it is ready to paint.

5 ▶ When the paint is dry, pop the balloon by cutting off the end with the string tied to it. You could decorate your animal with eyes, a mouth or a tail.

Decoration ideas

Plume, fin or tail
Cut this shape from card.
Fold the flaps,
one backwards,
one forwards.
Stick them down
on to your animal.

Eyes
Stick paper circles together.

Magazine Cut-outs

Cut out pictures from old magazines and catalogues and use them to make a new picture of your own.

You will need

old magazines and catalogues

cold-water paste and brush

round-ended scissors

hole punch

plain paper

ribbon

1 Choose pictures of people, children, animals or toys and cut them out. Sort the pictures into sets.

2 ▶ Arrange the cut-outs on the plain paper. Stick them down with cold-water paste when you have decided where you want them to go.

3 ▶ Cut out a hat, a head, a body, legs and feet from 5 different people. Mix them up and put them together again to make a funny figure.

Collecting pictures

Put your sets of pictures into envelopes and mark the front TOYS, CHILDREN, ANIMALS or PEOPLE. Use them for making cards, or decorating your pictures or play hats.

4 ▶ Make a book of funny figures. Punch holes in the side of the pictures and tie them together with ribbon. Give all the figures silly names like Molly Mixture and Wobbly Wilbur.

Brightly Coloured Butterflies

Brighten up your room with a display of colourful butterflies.

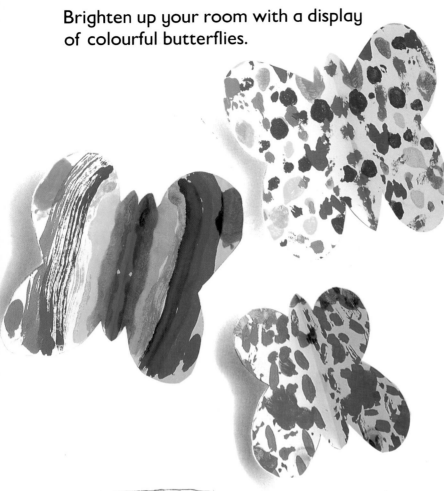

1 Spread some newspaper. Mix red, yellow and blue paints with a little cold-water paste to thicken them. Keep the colours apart so they don't run into each other.

2 Cut rectangles of white paper into different sizes to make big, middle-sized and small butterflies. Fold them in half.

3 Start at the folded centre and draw half of the body and one side of a butterfly's wings on the paper. Cut out the butterfly shape and open it out.

5 Try choosing just 2 of the primary colours, (red, blue and yellow,) to make your pattern. What happens when you press the wings together and the colours mix? You have a new colour!

4 Paint a pattern on 1 side of the butterfly. Fold it in half and press the 2 sides together to print the pattern on to both wings. Stick your butterfly on a wall.

Brighten up your room

Use up your mixed paints by painting flowers on a large piece of paper. Stick on some small butterflies, leaving the wings free.

Stick a large butterfly on to the window where it will catch the light.

Play Hats

Make a collection of hats for dressing-up.
They are lots of fun and easy to make.

You will need

coloured card
and paper

masking tape

pencil

felt-tip pens

ruler

cotton wool

round-ended
scissors

milk bottle
tops

thick glue
and brush

sparkly bits
and pieces

Animal hats

Use brown card
with round ears
for a mouse,

pink card with
leaf-shaped ears
for a pig,

grey card with
enormous ears
for an elephant,
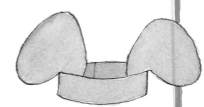

black card with
triangle ears for
a cat. Use face
paints to give
yourself a pink
nose and whiskers.

1 ▶ To make a hat band, cut a strip of card about 6 cm wide, and long enough to go round your head. Use different coloured card for each hat you make.

3 ▶ Draw a skull and cross-bones on white card. Give it black eyes and teeth. Cut out and stick on to half a circle of black card. Stick the black card on to a black hat band.

2 ▶ Measure the strip of card round your head. Overlap the 2 ends and stick them together with masking tape to make a circle which fits comfortably.

4 ▶ Cut zig-zag shapes from a wider hat band to make a crown. Stick on cotton wool and sparkly bits and pieces to look like jewels.

A Mixed Salad Tree

Keep old or dried-out fruit and vegetables to print an exotic tree for a wall hanging.

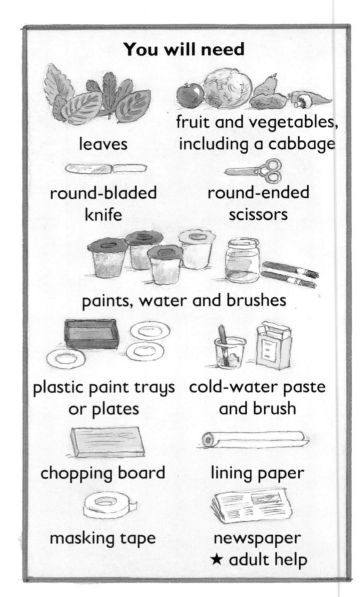

You will need

leaves

fruit and vegetables, including a cabbage

round-bladed knife

round-ended scissors

paints, water and brushes

plastic paint trays or plates

cold-water paste and brush

chopping board

lining paper

masking tape

newspaper

★ adult help

This long piece is for the tree.

So this one must be for the leaf, fruit and vegetable prints.

1 ▶ Lay plenty of newspaper out on the floor. Roll out and cut 1 long and 1 shorter piece of lining paper over the newspaper. Stick the ends down firmly with tape.

2 Mix brown and some brightly coloured paints with some cold-water paste to thicken them. Pour the paint into plastic trays or plates.

4 Dip a piece of cabbage into the brown paint, then press it down on to the large sheet of paper to make a print. Print it over and over again to make the trunk and branches of a tree.

3 ★ Cut the fruit and vegetables in half. Hold each one steady with one hand and cut well away from your fingers. Cut as straight as you can. Cut a small cabbage into quarters.

5 Paint the leaves bright colours, then press them paint side down on to the smaller piece of paper. Dip the fruit and vegetable halves in the paint and print them too. Cut them out and stick on to your tree.

More decorations

Make some brightly coloured birds using collage and some butterflies to put on the tree.

A Weather Chart

What's the weather like today? Open the windows of your weather chart to record the weather.

You will need

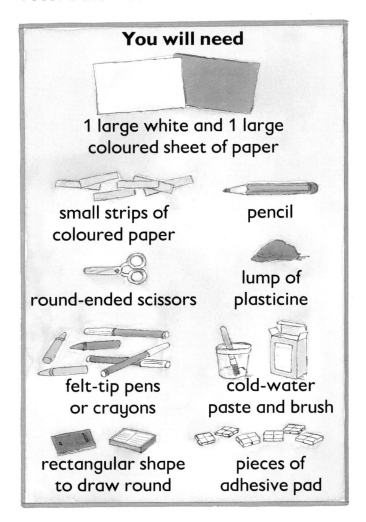

1 large white and 1 large coloured sheet of paper

small strips of coloured paper

pencil

round-ended scissors

lump of plasticine

felt-tip pens or crayons

cold-water paste and brush

rectangular shape to draw round

pieces of adhesive pad

1 Find a rectangular shape like a small note book or a tape box. Draw round it 6 times on the coloured paper, leaving a space between each shape, to make 6 windows.

This week's weather

Make a chart to record what sort of weather we are having this week.

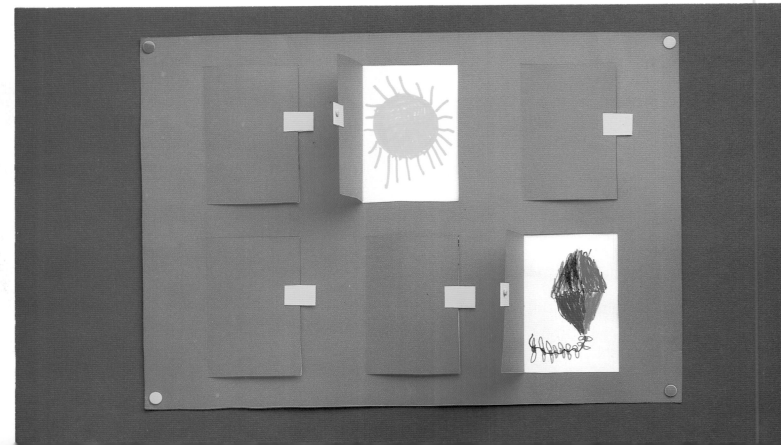

2 Stick a little bit of plasticine under the pencil outline of a window. Push your scissors through the paper into the plasticine underneath.

3 Cut and fold open all the windows. Put the coloured paper on top of the white paper and draw round the inside of the windows to make matching rectangular shapes on the white paper.

4 Draw different weather pictures in each rectangle. Open the windows. Stick the coloured paper on to the white.

5 Label the windows to match your weather pictures. Cut 6 small strips of coloured paper. Fold each one in half and stick to the edge of each window to make a handle. Write 'What's the weather like today?' across the top of the chart.

A Cardboard Train

Save some big cardboard boxes to make a train with trailers and a signal box.

Take your favourite toys for a ride.

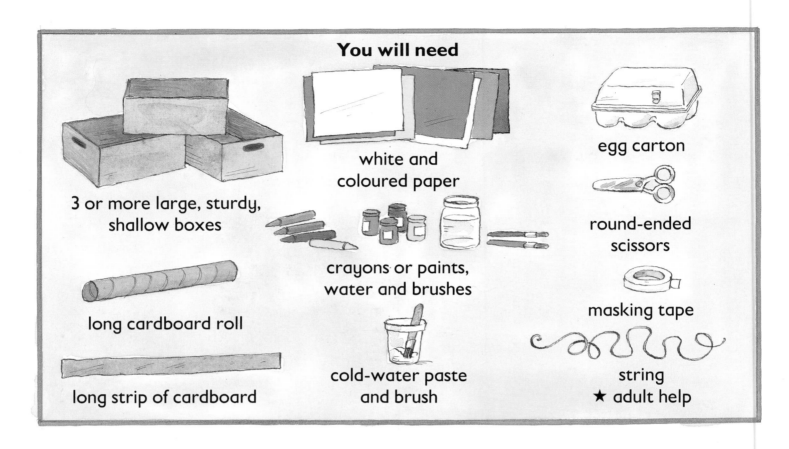

You will need

3 or more large, sturdy, shallow boxes

long cardboard roll

long strip of cardboard

white and coloured paper

crayons or paints, water and brushes

cold-water paste and brush

egg carton

round-ended scissors

masking tape

string
★ adult help

1 Take 2 boxes. Hold one upright and the other flat. Push the flat one inside the upright one to make an L shape. Tape the sides together.

2 Draw the view that the engine driver sees from his cabin and stick it on the inside of the upright box. Draw a picture of yourself driving the train and stick it on the outside.

3 To make a lever, hold the cardboard roll upright against the side of the box and put the cardboard strip over it. Fix the strip with masking tape. Stick STOP and GO labels beside it. Cut and paint wheels and buffers and stick them in place.

4 Stick coloured paper knobs on to the bottom of an egg carton to make a control panel. Use tape to fix it underneath the window in the cabin.

5 Use more boxes for the trailers.
★ Attach them to the train with string threaded through each box and knotted. Put your passengers on board.

Make a signal box

★ Cut a circle in a cardboard box. Fit a cardboard roll into it. Cut 3 round shapes from white folded paper. Colour red, yellow and green circles on them for lights. Take turns to work the signals and drive the train.

My Book

A book of your own is fun to make. You can put whatever you choose in it.

I'm drawing myself in my favourite tee-shirt.

I'm making creepy blue hand-prints!

You will need

For the book

sheets of coloured paper

paints, water and brushes
or felt-tip pens

old plate

thick glue
and brush

newspaper

For the binding

ribbon or ring binder

hole punch ★ adult help

1 ▶ With the coloured paper make some pages about yourself. Start with a photograph or make a self-portrait. Mix some paint on an old plate and make some hand, foot and finger prints. Wash yourself afterwards!

2 Write your height, weight and birthday. Draw your favourite food, toys and television programmes. Stick in pictures of your family and friends.

3 When your book is ready punch 2 holes in each page and tie them with ribbon.
★ Or you could clip the pages into a ring binder. Stick a photograph on the front and write MY BOOK by: write in your own name.

Collecting souvenirs

When you go on holiday or on an outing, look out for small souvenirs. Keep brochures, menus, postcards, paper napkins or badges to put in your book.

Put on a Play

You can use some of the things you have learned to make to put on a play with your friends.

Here are some ideas

▶ Make characters so that each of you can play a part.

Use your Play Hats (page 22).

Make a witch's hat from black paper.

Add a big star to a blue hat band to make a fairy's hat.

Make a wand from a thin roll of newspaper wrapped in kitchen foil. Add a black star for a wicked wizard or a yellow star for a good fairy.

▶ Try on some masks made from paper plates and cardboard rolls. Make holes for eyes.

▶ You can make garlands and necklaces from crumpled tissue paper, cotton reels, bright coloured buttons and pasta. Thread them all on to thin string.

▶ Now decide where you want your play to be set. It might be in a forest, on a farm, in a fairy castle, on a desert island or in a snowy country.

▶ Make up a story and act it for an audience. Try a Christmas Play, an Easter Play or a Birthday Play.

Have fun!